HEAL TH CARE ISSUES OF

Aging Families

A Handbook for Aging Parents

A Fire Drill

for Building Strength and Flexibility in Families

W0008293

John W. Gibson, DSW
Bonnie Brown Hartley, Ph.D.

To the memory of my older sister Patsy and my mom.
And to my younger sister Shirley and my dad, who faced our family's
health care challenges with love, courage, and endurance.
— John W. Gibson

To Lane, with love and gratitude.
— Bonnie Brown Hartley

Table of Contents

Fire Drills help one prepare for change. This *Fire Drill* is for anyone—aging parent or adult child—who wishes to learn about and prepare for health care issues related to aging.

Dealing with aging and its various accompanying changes—some gradual and barely perceptible, others sudden and shocking—has been a theme in our consulting practices for more than three decades. There also have been personal challenges for each of us that have influenced how we approach this topic personally and professionally. We know what a difference it can make to face and prepare for these unwanted changes in physical and mental health and abilities, as well as the often unwelcome needs that accompany them.

So this *Fire Drill,* with its accompanying questions, assignments, suggested activities and reading, focuses on health changes in the context of aging and their impact on families and their individual members. It provides resources that will make it possible for us to face the changes that inevitably come with age and minimize their disruptive impact.

Introduction

Health Care Issues for Aging Families is part of a four-volume series of handbooks focusing on different areas of interest to aging families: family dynamics, health care issues, legal issues and financial issues. Because a reader may begin the series with any one of these four handbooks, some of the core concepts must be introduced in each one. If you have used one of the other handbooks, this introductory material and certain other portions of the book may be very similar to what you have already read, and you might want to skip ahead to the core of the topic at hand. Do read the Scenario for Aging Parents (or Adult Children) in each of the handbooks, because it is geared specifically to that individual handbook's topic.

For Aging Parents and Their Adult Children

We will all age. Through our observations and experiences, we know that we will decline, but there is much we can do to prepare for and meet the changes, challenges and opportunities that come with our own aging and that of those closest to us. The authors' own lives, and those of the countless families we have been privileged to know over the years, have taught us the value of preparing for probable changes and challenges as well as the value of cultivating habits of thinking and behavior

A few of us imagine we'll be like the one out of 20 older adults who remain relatively healthy, able-bodied, and sound of mind and who die peacefully in their sleep at a relatively advanced age—having enjoyed the preceding day in relative good health.

that will allow us to optimally respond to unexpected and unwanted changes and challenges.

John relates how this came home to him, about 10 years ago:

> *When my father turned 75, he took the opportunity at this milestone in his life—"having lived three quarters of a century"—to reflect on, among other things, the care he gave to his wife, my mom, following her stroke and during the last few years of her life. What I remember most were my father's words through a choking-up voice: "Why didn't someone tell us what was ahead?" "Why were we so unprepared?" Our family was unprepared for the hard times that were to come.*

To be sure there have been many, many good times in John's father's life, and aging has not diminished those. However, the truth is that most of us in our 60s, 70s, and 80s don't anticipate and prepare for our own growing frailty and the loss of ability to function that, to various degrees, usually

We know that time is of the essence, and we can no longer view it as extending indefinitely into the future.

accompanies advancing age. A few of us imagine we'll be like the one out of 20 older adults who remain relatively healthy, able-bodied, and sound of mind and who die peacefully in their sleep at a relatively advanced age—having enjoyed the preceding day in relative good health.

However, from our experience older adults simply do not honestly and seriously face what will most probably befall us before we pass on. If we have avoided thinking about our own aging, we are ill-prepared to make sound decisions based on a careful weighing of personal and family values, personal and family physical, social and financial assets, and the larger context and community in which we reside.

This *Fire Drill* handbook offers insights from many who have faced such changes and challenges.[1] Further, it poses hard questions for us to consider, provides important checklists to help us prepare, and suggests courses of action and resources to strategically guide our actions. We know that time is of the essence, and we can no longer view it as extending indefinitely into the future. Therefore this handbook attempts to be brief, offering only what the authors think are the bare bones, while providing lots of "next step" resources for going deeper into any area related to health care issues and aging.

> **Today's longer life expectancy means you may live more years, both of good health and of fragility and family interdependence, than you ever expected.**

Today's longer life expectancy means you may live more years, both of good health and of fragility and family interdependence, than you ever expected. The trend over the past century toward smaller families could mean that the care you may need must be spread across fewer sons and daughters. More women in the workforce means more daughters face the multiple demands and stresses of work, family and caregiving. On the other hand, increasing numbers of sons and husbands are taking on the responsibility of caregiving. More blended families exist, where people who each have children have remarried and combined families. This results in more complex relationships across and within generations over such issues as trust, responsibility, loyalty, caregiving, etc. Knowing where to turn may not be as simple as in the past.

---

[1] *Fire Drills*, created by one of the authors of this handbook and used with positive results over the past decade, are exercises to build supportive contingency plans for significant change: e.g., sudden death or catastrophic illness of a loved one, unexpected loss (or gain) of wealth, or career uncertainties. *Fire Drills* incorporate information tracking with brainstorming, both of which help us meet the unknown.

There is great value in bravely and openly thinking about aging because it allows your grown children the unique opportunity to begin preparing, at an even earlier age, for their own aging. You can model self-honesty, courage, and preparation for wanted as well as unplanned and unwanted changes in your future. Your adult children will learn from your example. Aging parents have much to offer their adult children through the way they face, react to, and live their later years. We urge you to once again serve as a model for your children in how to deal with what lies ahead for them.

> **You can model self-honesty, courage, and preparation for wanted as well as unplanned and unwanted changes in your future. Your adult children will learn from your examples.**

You will note that this handbook has two distinct parts: one for aging parents and one for the adult children of aging parents. This introduction is substantially the same in both. You will also notice there is only one bibliography, found at the end of the section geared to adult children. The decision to place it there was arbitrary. We intend the bibliography for both parts of the handbook because its contents will be helpful to the family as a whole.

The organizational structure of the two parts is roughly the same because they are designed to be used hand in hand. However, there are some differences in text based on the target audience. These two stakeholder groups—aging parents and their adult children—have different needs, perspectives and experience. You will see that some questions are geared specifically to adult children in their section of this handbook while the questions geared to you as their parents are somewhat different. The *Fire Drill* scenarios also differ just slightly to reflect the different perspectives of aging parents and their adult children. In addition, you will notice that the type is larger in the section for parents.

Finally, you will see that we have inverted the parents' part of the handbook. Our reason for doing this is to emphasize the power of perspective. Aging parents and their adult children may look at the same challenge or experience from perspectives that seem 180 degrees apart. Since the printed page is not three-dimensional, we couldn't demonstrate that difference viscerally. So inverting one of the two parts at least gives the reader a visual reminder of those differences. One perspective is not better than the other. Neither is right nor wrong. They're just different.

In her book *Creative Aging*, elder author Mary Baird Carlsen describes how she continues to actively search for attitudes, beliefs, behaviors and habits that will help her age well, that will help her find opportunities amidst the losses as she ages and help her see new possibilities remaining in her life, while avoiding the powerful pull of becoming preoccupied with physical changes, limitations, aches, pains, and worse. Carlsen intends to continue to have dreams and set goals while recognizing that she has reduced capacities and fewer years remaining.

The authors created this handbook because we believe we must all actively and deliberately try to make our later years our best years, while also planning for and dealing with changes and challenges. This handbook, with its questions, assignments, suggested reading and activities, will help you and your family courageously face various changes in health and ability that inevitably come with age. By facing and preparing for these changes we can lessen their disruptive impact on our lives, thus allowing more time, energy, flexibility and money to devote to those people and activities that mean the most to us.

We ask you to not just read this book, but to *use it*.

I: Getting Started

This *Fire Drill* handbook, intended for older adults, will facilitate the gathering of valuable knowledge and resources ahead of time so you can quickly and optimally respond to health changes and challenges. What is important is to clarify your own thoughts and values while becoming as knowledgeable as possible about the health care issues that arise during the aging process, what resources are available to you, and what you can do to prepare.

The questions and the tasks to complete throughout this handbook are meant to be considered and discussed with your spouse and adult children. Exploratory dialogue with a trusted family member or friend can help you understand your own choices and preferences.

> **We have witnessed couples, together for 50 years or more, who when discussing their answers with each other are surprised by how differently their spouse or sibling answered an item.**

For couples or siblings living together, based on the authors' combined 50-plus years of experience, we recommend that each of you individually answer the questions posed throughout the *Fire Drill*. We have witnessed couples, together for 50 years or more, who when discussing their answers with each other are surprised by how differently their spouse or sibling answered an item. There remains much to learn about the person you have chosen for your spouse or who is a life-long sibling. We invite you to learn even more about this person you've known for so long.

While many in the western world think and operate from mental models of independence, autonomy, self-control and self-direction, what becomes clear to many of us as we grow older and begin to address the questions posed in

Families can grow stronger, improve communication, and become more resilient.

this *Fire Drill* is that we are interdependent. The decisions we make regarding our own aging, and our actions or lack of action, can directly impact our family whether we want this or not. One of the best ways to shape this powerful impact—that is, to minimize the negative impact and maximize the positive impact—is by thoughtfully answering these questions and gathering the necessary information. And by talking with your spouse, adult children, or involved friends and relatives about these topics, you will impact them and your relationship with them in very positive ways.

Finally, we have seen again and again that families and their patterns of interaction can and do change. Families can grow stronger, improve communications, and become more resilient. However, it is a slow process. Your family has developed and become what it is over decades. You can't expect big changes quickly.

The following information about *Fire Drills*, Life Cycles and Generational Differences, and Guiding Principles for Aging Families is included in each book in this series. If you have read one of the other handbooks and prefer not to review this information here, please skip ahead to the Scenario for Aging Parents in this section.

Why Do Fire Drills?

This Aging Family Handbook Series uses a *Fire Drill* model as a road map to help families identify and prepare for the impact of aging. But you may wonder why *Fire Drills* are worth the effort. Aging families need to learn how to manage transitions together. However, aging families are not by definition "teams." Often family members need to address unarticulated assumptions about their own multiple roles in the family, e.g., as parent and aging spouse, or as adult child and parent. Family members need to learn how to nurture a vision and a sense of purpose that can be understood and supported by all generations.

> **Family members need to learn how to nurture a vision and a sense of purpose that can be understood and supported by all generations.**

While working with business families who struggle with issues around ownership and management succession, the authors found the *Fire Drill* format uniquely effective as a way to begin a process that allows people to shift their attitudes, beliefs, and expectations around three core elements of change: money, power and love—what we have called a family's "Bermuda triangle." The way your own family chooses to blend these either strengthens or destroys your family's relationships and ability to manage change.

The attitudes, beliefs and expectations that influence our lives and our relationships—whether at home, at school, at work, or in our communities—seem to grow out of unspoken (and often unrecognized) assumptions about money, power and love. Some of these assumptions may be a product of the particular phase of life, or life cycle, in which you and other family members find yourselves.

For example, assumptions about money may need to be tested as we age. We may limit our expectations about what is possible in terms of retirement options based on the constraints of our early years' financial circumstances. People who grew up in the Great Depression are careful about throwing away leftovers, turning off lights, and saving for a rainy day. They sometimes put off finalizing estate plans because they worry that another economic crash might leave them living in their car or on the street in such a worst-case scenario. Taking the time to work through the details of available resources in a variety of circumstances may help such a person get past the barriers to change erected by those early assumptions about financial needs and constraints.

In addition, as you likely have noticed, generational differences can profoundly influence assumptions and influence the way members of your family relate to one another and approach change. Learning more about life cycles and differences in generations will enhance your understanding of your family.

Life Cycles and Generational Differences

As we age, we pass from one life period or life stage into the next; these life cycles may be understood as personal stories. Each personal story, at each stage, has both unique features and universal characteristics. We will describe here some life cycle concepts that are helpful in understanding multigenerational families. We also provide some questions for you to answer about your own multigenerational family and a set of principles that will aid cross-generational communication.

We particularly wish to call your attention to the way in which an individual's perspectives reveal a complex interplay between unique influences in the individual's life and more universal patterns of influence.

There are no simple answers. This is what makes us endlessly fascinating to each other as human beings—and also what makes us so maddeningly difficult to understand. We believe the concepts, perspectives, and questions presented here will give you valuable tools for the challenging but rich task of understanding the dynamics of your aging family.

Personality and Life Cycle

An early and comprehensive theory of personality development is Erik Erikson's "Eight Stages of Man." [2] Erikson viewed the person we are at any point in our lives as being a result of the individual, societal and historical forces that shape our lives. He posited that each stage of development offers a major conflict or challenge, and that if we successfully meet that challenge a unique strength arises. If we do not resolve the conflict or meet the challenge, then we are left without that strength. Furthermore, the unresolved conflict might play itself out in disruptive ways throughout our lives, or until we are able to meet that developmental challenge and gain the strength its mastery gives us.

Erikson's eight stages, along with the conflict to be resolved and the strength to be gained with its successful resolution, are shown in Table 1.

---

[2] See E. H. Erikson's *Identity and the Life Cycle*, chapters 1, 10, 14, and *The Life Cycle Completed*, chapters 9, 10, 14.

STAGE	CONFLICT	STRENGTH GAINED
I. Infancy	Basic Trust vs. Basic Mistrust	Hope
II. Early Childhood	Autonomy vs. Shame	Doubt
III. Play Age	Initiative vs. Guilt	Purpose
IV. School Age	Industry vs. Inferiority	Competence
V. Adolescence	Identity vs. Identity Confusion	Fidelity
VI. Young Adulthood	Intimacy vs. Isolation	Love
VII. Adulthood	Generativity vs. Stagnation	Care
VIII. Old Age	Integrity vs. Despair	Wisdom

Table 1: Erikson's Eight Life Stages

Because the way in which each of these conflicts is resolved, or not resolved, impacts all later stages, in Erikson's view we cannot truly understand people without knowing their unique life story. For example, the way in which an infant learns basic trust will have some impact on the nature of that individual's faith and ability to hope much later in life. On the other hand, he believes we all face these basic conflicts. Thus, the unique exists within the universal.

Generational Factors

The generation into which we are born is another factor that contributes to our individual uniqueness. Each generation of a family has been influenced by certain historical and cultural events and beliefs, and so each generation might be expected to have differing values and models for how the world works. Many believe that our behavior is most strongly impacted by events and culture during our teens, since during this stage of life we are simultaneously formulating values and creating internal mental models to help us understand how the world works.

Table 2 depicts five generations, the years covered, current age span, a few significant historical events, and some common values seen as resulting from those experiences.

Generation	Born	Current Age Range (2006)	Significant Events	Values
WWII	1909–1932	74–97	Great Depression (1929) WWII (1941)	Duty before Pleasure, Dedication, Sacrifice
Swing Generation	1933–1945	61–73	Korean War (1950) McCarthy HCUAA Hearings (1954) Civil Rights Act (1957)	Patience, Loyalty, Delayed Reward
Boomers	1946–1964	42–60	John Glenn Circles the Earth (1962) President Kennedy Assassinated (1963) National Organization of Women (1966) ML King & RF Kennedy Assassinated (1968)	Optimism, Cooperation, Personal Gratification, Youthfulness
Generation X	1965–1976	30–41	Arab Terrorists at Munich Olympics (1972) Watergate Scandal (1974) Mass Suicide in Jonestown (1978) Three Mile Island Nuclear Accident (1979) U.S. Corporations Begin Massive Layoffs (1979)	Can't Trust Others, Flexibility, Freedom, Autonomy
Generation Y	1977–1994	12–29	Oklahoma City Bombings (1995) Mother Theresa, Princess Diana deaths (1997) Clinton/Lewinsky Scandal (1998) Columbine High School Massacre (1999)	People Will Take Advantage of You, Civic Duty, Morality, Street Smarts

Table 2: Generational Factors

Health Care Issues of Aging Families: A Handbook for Aging Parents

An awareness of the historical events that shaped the lives of these different generations helps us understand the "different places we're coming from." For example, Generation-Xers are noted for being resistant to trusting others. So, rather than taking Generation-X family members' distrust of you personally, look at the major historical deceptions to which they were exposed. It makes sense that they would be wary. Generation-Xers witnessed massive corporate layoffs of their loyal parents. In contrast, WWII and Swing generation members came of age when loyalty, hard work and delayed gratification were rewarded.

If generational influences are not considered, the clash of different values and different models of how the world works may lead to conflicts between generations that could at times become very personal and sometimes even ugly. However, as was the case with life stages, the unique exists within the universal. Within each generation, an individual also is influenced by the impact of his or her unique family, education, and life events.

We urge you to use these concepts and perspectives to guide you in understanding your multigenerational family and its unique interactions. We have only scratched the surface of factors that shape who we are, what we value and believe, and how this impacts our interactions with other family members. While there is so much more to know about multigenerational family dynamics, the following questions can start you on the path toward better understanding your own family.

Questions for Reflection:
- Who comprises your multigenerational family? (List all members.)

- To what generation does each belong?

- What differences in values, work ethics, ideas about money, etc., can you see that might result from generational differences?

- How old and in what life stage is each family member?

- What do you believe are the most pressing issues that concern each family member at this point in his or her life?

- What current or possible future conflicts do you see regarding the concerns and issues individual family members are facing?

- What are some ways you can learn more about the values, beliefs and world views that other family members hold?

- Identify some of the unique experiences, events and circumstances that have shaped who they are, what they believe, value, hope and fear.

- How are the generations in your family different? How are they similar?

Guiding Principles for Aging Families

We offer the following suggestions as guiding principles, to support your ability to have a positive influence on your multigenerational family communication.

- Seek first to understand the other. He or she may be more interesting and complex than you think.

- Identify the universal patterns and then look for the unique expression in each family member. There will be more factors contributing to each person's behavior than you think.

- Cultivate and develop a curiosity about family members' life history, however short or long, and the memories that were and are important to them.

- Don't take conflicts due to generational differences personally! It's amazing—given all the differences that shape who we are and our poorly developed ability to describe these differences—that we ever agree at all.

- Get comfortable explaining the range of principles and values you and your family hold so that you are able to explain them to others.

- With broader and deeper understanding of another family member, we can find more areas of difference and more common ground. Find both.

- Remember that conversations among multiple generations are complex. Keep them as *"and"* conversations rather than *"us* vs. *them."*

This handbook includes questions about what you personally may believe, want, or direct. In addition to asking questions for you to consider, we also ask if you have discussed your thoughts on these topics with loved ones. Yet we understand that people differ in the way they come to conclusions. Some of you may choose to identify your values, wishes and directions before any discussions with loved ones, some only after discussions with loved ones. Others may go back and forth between personal soul searching and discussions with loved ones before arriving at conclusions.

> **What is important is to clarify your own thoughts and values, and plan ahead accordingly.**

For the sake of simplicity we have used the terms *spouse* and *adult children* throughout this handbook. In certain situations, you may have a trusted loved one in your same generation with whom you might wish to discuss your thoughts on these questions. That's fine. Also, you may not have adult children, or you may be estranged from them and choose not to discuss your wishes and thoughts with them. That's fine. If it is appropriate in your situation to talk with next generation family members outside of your immediate family who care about you, i.e., nieces and nephews, or to skip a generation and talk with your grandchildren, that's fine. What is important is to clarify your own thoughts and values, and plan ahead accordingly.

Scenario for Aging Parents

The following scenario and accompanying questions, based on typical situations that arise in aging families, are intended to stimulate thinking about similar situations you may face.

Joe and Mary have been married for 35 years. Their four children are all married with young children and live out of state; they all graduated from college and have good jobs. Joe and Mary are both retired, and have always thought their pensions would be adequate for their modest lifestyle needs. Two days ago, Mary had a stroke. Her prognosis for partial recovery is excellent. She will go to a rehabilitation center when she is released from the hospital. When she returns to their home, Joe says he'll be able to look after his wife by himself, with just a little support from home health nurses. Joe called to tell his oldest daughter Terry today, two days after the stroke. Terry was upset, and has arranged to come home tomorrow. She also contacted her three siblings, who will arrive the day after tomorrow.

Having read this typical scenario, please answer the following questions.

Personal Questions:

- Does Joe realize all that may be involved in caring for Mary at home during her continued recovery and treatment, and with the irreversible limitations the doctors anticipate? What might be involved?

- How might Joe's activities change? How might Joe's daily life change?

• Given their traditional roles, what decision-making responsibilities might Joe need to assume for the first time?

• What potential conflicts might Joe face with health care professionals: e.g., home health nurses, speech therapists, insurance companies, and government agencies?

Intra-generational Questions:

• How might Mary's life change if she does not fully recover?

• How might Joe and Mary discuss the impact of Mary's stroke on them each personally, and as a couple?

• What decisions might Joe need to assume that previously were made by Mary or jointly, and how might Mary's desire and ability to make decisions change during her recovery?

- What potential conflicts might arise over time between Joe and Mary?

Intergenerational Questions:
- How might Joe and Mary feel about all four of their adult children showing up from out of town a few days after Mary's stroke?

- How might Joe and Mary's desire to protect their children from additional expenses and worry impact Joe and Mary's health and quality of life?

- How might Joe and Mary react to the well-meaning suggestions of their adult children?

- How might Joe and Mary resolve potential conflicts with their adult children while maintaining family harmony?

- How might their children feel about the fact that Joe waited two days after Mary's stroke before calling them?

II: Building Blocks for Decision Making

The Impact of Aging on Health Care Decisions[3]

Physical and mental changes related to aging affect all aspects of life. And as we grow older our moods, our minds and our bodies become more intertwined. Changes in our bodies such as loss of hearing, moving more slowly, or not sleeping well, for example, affect our mood and our mental functioning, and vice versa.

In our handbook *The Dynamics of Aging Families* we describe how the various changes that normally come with aging impact us and our relationships with family members. In this handbook we provide a brief outline of common physical changes that come with aging, system by system, and pass on some suggestions other older adults have found helpful in minimizing the impact of these changes. Learning more about the changes in mind, body and emotions that typically accompany aging can help us understand and prepare for them.

Age-Related Changes

Vision Changes

- Loss of the ability to see images clearly (visual acuity) as the lens of the eye becomes denser and cloudier.

- Decreasing ability to focus on items close-up (presbyopia) as the lens of the eye becomes more rigid. Individuals who are nearsighted will need bifocals.

---

[3] This information is not intended to replace the advice of any professional (attorney, accountant, financial planner, health care provider, geriatric care manager, insurance broker, or therapist). Anyone who wishes to embark on any of the change management options described herein should first consult with qualified professional advisors familiar with their unique needs and circumstances.

- Blues, greens, and violets are harder to distinguish as the yellowing of the lens distorts color vision.

- Loss of side vision as the retina changes and narrows the field of vision.

- Difficulty adapting to and seeing in the dark as the pupil becomes smaller with age.

- Eyes are less able to adapt to glare.

- Eye diseases such as macular degeneration (which results in the loss of central vision), glaucoma (results in the loss of peripheral vision), keratoconus (the thinning of the cornea), and cataracts can seriously impair vision and are more common with age.

- If you develop diabetes, you may experience a loss of visual acuity.

> **Learning more about the changes in mind, body and emotions that typically accompany aging can help us understand and prepare for them.**

Suggestions:

- Schedule regular eye exams.

- Watch for behaviors suggesting vision problems, such as squinting, confusion, rubbing the eye, shutting/covering one eye, tilting/thrusting the head, holding objects closer.

- Avoid using clear glasses, cups, and plates; use bright (e.g., yellow, orange, red) and contrasting colors.

- Use contrasting colors or different textures at stairs and other places where needed, to accommodate declines in depth perception. Avoid glass tabletops.

- Increase lighting levels, and arrange lights to focus on individual tasks. Multiple sources of light are best.

- Use nightlights and large print books.

- Allow time for your eyes to adjust to changes in light.

- Reduce glare by using dull instead of highly polished finishes on furniture and floors.

- Sit where you can minimize glare in your eyes.

Hearing Changes

- Hearing changes generally occur in men at a younger age than in women.

- High-pitched tones become harder to hear, especially for men. The onset of this condition, called presbycusis, often occurs when men are in their mid-50s. It worsens with age.

- Presbycusis results in the "cocktail party effect." It becomes more difficult to listen to one person's voice when there is a lot of background noise.

Suggestions:

- Be alert for indications of hearing loss such as boosting the television volume, speaking loudly, withdrawing from social situations.

- Periodically check for cerumen (wax) in the ears. This can dramatically reduce hearing.

- An audiologist can remove wax built up over months or years.

- Presbycusis may be correctable with a hearing aid.

- Look directly at the person who is speaking.

- Speak clearly and slowly in deeper tones, and move your lips. We all gradually learn to lip read as we age.

- To converse, find a quiet place with minimum background noise.

- Give yourself time to sort out what you have heard. Ask, if it's unclear.

Taste And Smell Changes

- Taste buds wither and our sense of taste is reduced as we age.

- The senses of sweet and sour taste are lost first. The sense of bitter taste remains the longest.

- The sense of smell may also diminish, which reduces our enjoyment of food.

- The thirst mechanism, which reminds us to drink water, may decline, resulting in dehydration and accompanying dizziness. Dehydration can also be a cause of constipation.

Suggestions:

- Use more seasoning on foods, but avoid salt because it can cause a number of problems.

- Recognize that change in taste may partly be related to medication or to illness, and that your ability to taste may return later.

- Make sure that liquid intake is sufficient to prevent dehydration.

- Make sure smoke detectors are working.

- Check for spoiled food.

Skin Changes

- The skin becomes thinner and dryer and develops wrinkles.

- The loss of the layer of fat just below the skin decreases the ability to stay warm in cooler temperatures. We lose our "insulation." Hypothermia is more common as we age.

- We sweat less, so the sweat glands lose their ability to keep us cool in hotter temperatures. Overheating is more common as we age.

- The skin loses some of its ability to feel pain, or a light touch.

Suggestions:

- To prevent dry and flaky skin, thoroughly and gently rinse away soap.

- After bathing, thoroughly and gently pat dry rather then rub the skin. Apply moisturizing lotion.

- Those who cannot move by themselves should be frequently repositioned to prevent pressure sores where they are sitting or lying.

- Regularly check skin for dryness, pressure sores, cuts, and burns.

- Be aware of sudden changes in air temperature that cause discomfort because our bodies are slower to adjust, or can't adjust.

- Make sure hot and cold water faucets are easy to identify and easy to turn on and off, because as we age we feel heat less quickly. Turn hot water thermostats down. Monitor bath water and heating pad temperatures to prevent burning.

- For comfort, room temperatures may need to be warmer in the winter and cooler in the summer.

Muscle, Bone, and Joint Changes

- Muscle mass decreases and muscles lose their strength and tone with age.

- Joints become less mobile.

- The spinal cord shortens with age.

- As we age we are more likely to develop arthritis.

- Bones become more porous and break more easily (osteoporosis). Women are at greater risk for osteoporosis because of the loss of estrogen that occurs after menopause, but statistics show that men are also at risk.

- Age increases the need to monitor for osteoporosis.

Suggestions:

- Stay active. "Use it or lose it" is true!

- Get regular exercise, including weight bearing, aerobic and stretching.

- Implement safeguards such as stair railings, non-slip risers on stairs, and non-skid strips in bathtubs to prevent falls.

- Learn to use mobility aids such as canes and walkers appropriately to reduce the risk of injury and falls.

- Make sure seating is comfortable, but firm and not too deep, as well as high enough off the floor to allow ease in rising from the chair or sofa.

- Strategies for reducing osteoporosis include increased calcium intake, weight bearing exercises, and hormone replacement therapy. Both men and women should periodically have their bone density tested. Every adult should be tested to establish a baseline.

Heart and Blood Vessel Changes

- The heart rate decreases because the heart muscles get weaker and do not contract as quickly.

- When the heart rate becomes elevated, it takes longer for it to return to normal.

- Two factors cause the arteries to harden (become less elastic): 1) age-related calcification and 2) the build up of fat (cholesterol) on the artery walls, a condition called atherosclerosis.

Suggestions:

- Undertake activities at an appropriate pace. This may mean a more measured pace, or it may be that a slight increase in your activity level would build endurance. Ask your physician.

- Learn how to conserve your energy.

- Watch for signs of fatigue, decreased endurance, dizziness, confusion, and distress.

- Allow enough time between position changes (i.e., between sitting and standing, or lying and standing) to prevent dizziness.

- Place heavy objects at waist level or below to eliminate the need to lift them over your head.

- Engage in moderate exercise on a regular basis. See your physician before initiating an exercise program.

- Implement a diet that increases "good" cholesterol and reduces "bad" cholesterol.

- Get routine blood pressure tests, and implement a low-salt diet to reduce high blood pressure.

• Learn the signs and the symptoms of a heart attack, and of a stroke.

Lung Changes

- Our lungs become less elastic, reducing the amount of oxygen we take in. However, the limiting factor is less the ability of the lungs to take in oxygen than the ability of the heart to circulate it.

- Our breathing becomes less efficient, and our tolerance for exercise decreases.

Suggestions:

- Stop smoking and avoid secondhand smoke.

- Learn to breathe deeply, and practice it. Moderate exercise can help this.

- Slow the pace of your activities and allow more frequent rest periods.

- Learn your sources of stress, and reduce them.

- Make sure that you are eating properly and drinking enough fluids.

- Keep immunizations current for influenza, pneumonia, and other diseases that affect the lungs.

- Watch for signs of infection such as an increase in coughing, shortness of breath, colored sputum, and increased confusion.

Digestive System Changes

- With every decade, total calorie needs decline while the need for highly nutritious food increases.

- Indigestion and ulcers may increase because less gastric juice is being produced.

- The age-related decrease in saliva production increases the risk of gum (periodontal) disease.

Suggestions:

- Eat a balanced diet that includes high-fiber foods and healthy, nutrient-dense foods.

- Implement a regular schedule for using the toilet.

- Practice good oral hygiene and schedule periodic dental exams.

- Periodically evaluate dentures for good fit, and keep them clean. Poorly fitting dentures can cause soreness that limits one's ability to properly chew food. Discomfort may cause one to avoid nutritious foods that require chewing.

- If you have incontinence problems or problems with swallowing, have a medical evaluation.

Urinary System Changes

- Bladder capacity and muscle tone decrease, resulting in a need to urinate more frequently. However, urinary incontinence (the involuntary loss of urine) is not a normal part of aging.

- The kidneys become less efficient in removing wastes from the blood. Between the ages of 20 and 90, the kidney filtration rate drops by nearly 50 percent.

Suggestions:

- Make sure that toilet facilities are nearby and you can access them quickly.

- Remember to use the toilet frequently.

- Drink eight glasses of water/fluid each day unless restricted by doctor's orders.

- If you have incontinence problems, have them evaluated. For example, increased frequency of urination may be a symptom of diabetes or some other reversible condition.

- Be screened for prostate cancer and diabetes.

Glandular Changes

- The endocrine system's production of hormones (chemical messengers) decreases.

- The pancreas releases less insulin into the blood stream. This results in excess blood sugar and can lead to diabetes. Exercise, diet and weight control become even more important as we age.

- Hormones that stimulate the immune system begin to decrease. This decline is more gradual in males than in females.

- The ability to respond to stress decreases.

- The body's processes (metabolism) become less efficient.

- It is more difficult to maintain body temperature.

- Females experience the onset of menopause at approximately age 50, triggering reduced hormone production and the end of menstrual periods. Signs of menopause include thinning/drying of vaginal walls, hot flashes, sleep difficulty, and emotional changes.

- Testosterone production decreases during "male menopause," and men may experience depression, anxiety, and fatigue.

Suggestions:

- Learn as much as you can about hormonal changes that take place with age.

- Continue regular gynecological exams for women.

- Continue or establish regular prostate exams for men.

- Minimize physical, mental and emotional stress. Learn and practice daily some method of relaxation and stress reduction.

- Cultivate companionship, friendships, and social activities that are based on your true preferences. These enhance physical and emotional health.

- Dress carefully and in layers to avoid hypothermia (getting too cold) or heat stroke (getting too hot).

Sleep Pattern Changes

- There is a decrease in "sound" sleep.

- You are more likely to wake up during the night.

- The amount of time spent sleeping is reduced.

Suggestions:

- Develop a regular sleep routine.

- Reduce the intake of caffeine and fluids before bedtime.

- Limit the use of sleeping pills. Instead try other methods to promote sleep, such as relaxation techniques or warm milk.

- Watch for signs of sleep apnea, such as excessive daytime sleeping, behavioral disturbances, skill decline and disrupted sleep patterns.

Pharmacological Changes

- Changes in the liver, kidney and gastrointestinal systems affect your body's ability to absorb, distribute, and eliminate medications.

- The risk of side effects from medication increases with the number of drugs you take.

Suggestions:

- Make sure that every physician you see knows about all the medications and vitamin, mineral and herbal supplements you are taking.

- Have a complete, up-to-date list handy that specifies dosage and strength of each.

- Know what each medication does and what the possible side effects are.

- Watch for unexplained and unusual symptoms.

- Check for drug-to-drug interactions, food-to-drug interactions, and supplements-to-food-or-drug interactions.

Behavioral and Cognitive Changes

- With good health and plenty of use of our minds, complex problem-solving skills actually increase as we grow older. As do our vocabulary and our ability to understand and express subtle and nuanced points.

- Intelligence, or the ability to learn, does not necessarily decline when we age. Loss of intellectual abilities tends to be more related to low motivation, health problems and social isolation than to age.

- Our personality is pretty much the same throughout our life. However, our personality traits grow more prominent as we age.

- We may have more difficulty processing and organizing new information as we age. This also makes it more difficult to recall things.

- It is harder with age to recall people, places and things than it is to recognize them, because recognition is aided by what we see.

- Unexpressed grief can impact mental and emotional well-being as well as our physical well-being.

Suggestions:

- Establish routines in those activities of daily living you find most difficult. Make lists; maintain a daily log or journal.

- Use memory aids and familiar objects to help learn new tasks and remember old ones. Intentionally practice learning, remembering, and using your mind.[4]

- Develop interests that keep you involved in and challenged by life.

- Ask others to speak slowly, clearly and distinctly. Have the courage to make sure you understand and are understood.

- Ask simple questions and give simple instructions. Write down things you want to be sure to remember.

- Provide environmental cues (e.g., change the color of the walls and the flooring to differentiate areas; place a hook for your keys by the door).

- If you continue to be concerned about cognitive changes, arrange a clinical evaluation to rule out the many treatable conditions that often produce these symptoms (e.g., hypothyroidism, B-12 deficiency, stroke, kidney issues, liver and electrolyte disturbances, medication effects, depression, sensory changes, or sleep apnea).

- Recognize the mental, emotional and physical impact of grief on your health and well-being. Practice "healthy grieving."[5]

---

[4] See our handbook *The Dynamics of Aging Families* for more suggestions and helpful questions regarding issues of memory, reasoning and judgment.

[5] For suggestions and questions to help you address the impact of grief see *The Dynamics of Aging Families*. And to learn more about healthy grieving see some of the excellent texts in our bibliography, especially *As You Grieve* by Aaron Zerah and *Beyond Loss: A Practical Guide Through Grief to a Meaningful Life* by Lilly Singer, Margaret Sirot and Susan Rodd.

Health Care-Related Information to Have on Hand

When we are faced, gradually or suddenly, with the need to become more involved in the health care system, we need to gather all pertinent personal, financial, legal and health-related information. Important health care decisions can be very complex and can have financial, legal and family implications. Thinking things through in advance and collecting the information ahead of time makes it much easier to make the best decisions. This handbook will support you in that process.

> **Thinking things through in advance and collecting the information ahead of time makes it much easier to make the best decisions.**

First, here is an overview of tasks related to information gathering in order to prepare for anything, including an emergency:

- Begin with a list of lists.
- Work to complete each list.
- Begin to locate necessary information.
- Make notes of "to do" items.
- Keep your information safe (from fire, theft, etc.) and let someone you trust know where it is and how to access it.
- Update your information and create a backup system for it.

Personal Information

Personal Documents List

The first list we suggest you create is a Personal Documents List. The sample list on the next page is not comprehensive, but includes items you may wish to compile (and back up) so they are readily accessible to you, and to your trusted loved ones, when the need arises. Begin collecting this information now.

- Birth certificate
- Marriage certificate
- Divorce decrees of previous marriages
- Military records
- Cemetery deed
- Funeral instructions
- Income tax returns for the last six years
- Trust documents
- Pension and retirement plan documents
- House deeds/titles
- Mortgages
- Auto titles
- Powers of attorney
- Will and "Living Will"
- Medical directive/power of attorney
- Medicare card
- Medicare supplement policy
- Health and long-term care insurance
- Social Security card
- Homeowners' insurance
- Other personal and business documents

Many of us have a habit of being private about our personal, legal, health and financial issues. Consequently, we may be reluctant to share this information and perhaps even to gather and organize it for ourselves. We may not have realized that if a health crisis arises, this information will be needed.

Many of us have a habit of being private about our personal, legal, health and financial issues. Consequently, we may be reluctant to share this information and perhaps even to gather and organize it for ourselves.

Personal Support System List

The second list we recommend creating is a Personal Support System List. This is a list of people who would want to be informed in the event of a health problem or crisis, in order to help you.

In our independent, self-reliant society we often don't give much thought to whom we would ask for help, or whom we would inform if something happened to us. However, think for a moment about the people you love and care about. Imagine something happened to one of them. Wouldn't you want to know if a loved one was in the hospital, for example? John tells the following story about his own experience:

My father, now 81, was always a very proud, strong, self-reliant man. Sometimes I would find out, after the fact, that he'd had a health problem or a health scare. This upset me—I felt left out. I worried because if I didn't know, I couldn't give him help or support. Perhaps I played a little rough with my dad, but here's what I did. When I underwent laser surgery for a potentially serious eye problem, I deliberately did not tell him. Several weeks later, I let slip what I had undergone. As expected, Dad was mad—and no doubt hurt—that I had excluded him. I looked him straight in the eye and said, "Dad, I'll make you a deal. You know how you feel right now? Well, I've felt that way when you didn't tell me about some health problem, procedure or scare you had." I paused. "Dad, here's the deal. I'll promise to tell you, to keep you informed, if you will promise to keep me informed." He smiled, knowing I was right, admiring the tough man his boy had grown into, and still a bit angry at being left out.

So, begin collecting names, addresses, phone numbers, and email addresses:

- Relatives
- Friends
- Neighbors
- Physician
- Care manager
- Lawyer
- Pastor/Rabbi/Priest
- Accountant
- Banker
- Trust officer
- Stockbroker
- Financial planner and/or asset manager
- Insurance agent

> **In our independent, self-reliant society we often don't give much thought to whom we would ask for help, or whom we would inform if something happened to us. However, think for a moment about the people you love and care about.**

Financial Information

The need for financial information as it relates to health care issues is surprising and sometimes off-putting. Nonetheless, we have observed again and again that health care planning choices and decisions inevitably have financial impacts. And we have seen that when families are able to make choices and decisions with the knowledge of how the financial costs will impact them and their resources, they are happier with the decisions. They experience less stress in making choices, and less regret later, than if the choices were made without understanding the financial impact.

> **The need for financial information as it relates to health care issues is surprising and sometimes off-putting.**

Perhaps you are especially sensitive about sharing this information. In that case you may choose to begin, as some other older adults do, by gathering and organizing the information, and letting someone you trust completely know where it is located, but not sharing the information directly with them.

Financial Steps to Take Now

The three essential steps to take in pulling together your financial information are:

1. Inventory your resources and obligations.

2. Create your financial profile.

3. Simplify your routine financial transactions.

1. *Inventory Your Resources and Obligations*

Financial Resources:

- Banks (savings and checking accounts, CDs, savings bonds)
- Insurance
- Pensions and retirement plans
- Investments
- Deferred investments and shelters
- Real estate and business interests
- Valuables
- Other

Financial Obligations:

- Mortgages
- Auto loans
- Credit cards
- Personal debts (including loans you may have co-signed or guaranteed)
- Other

Income and Expenses:

- Statement of yearly income and expenses
- Statement of monthly income and expenses

2. *Create Your Financial Profile*

Your full financial profile will include the following:

- Resources and obligations list
- Yearly income and expenses statement

- Monthly income and expenses statement
- Net worth statement

3. *Simplify Your Routine Financial Transactions*

You can ease your mind and reduce work by simplifying your routine financial transactions. For example, you can pay regular bills such as mortgage or health insurance payments through automatic withdrawals or online; use online banking to balance checking accounts from anywhere; use Quicken or a similar program for recordkeeping. Some other possibilities will come to mind once you turn your attention to this.

You can ease your mind and reduce work by simplifying your routine financial transactions.

None of us likes to think that health care decisions are financially driven. For some they are not. But for many aging families, health care options—procedures, rehabilitation services and in-home care—must be weighed against the financial cost of those services. For more in-depth information about dealing with the financial issues aging families face, see our handbook *Financial Issues of Aging Families* (forthcoming, Summer 2007).

Legal Information

Never hesitate to seek legal advice when facing important health care issues that have legal implications. Better yet, anticipate what lies ahead and prepare thoughtfully and thoroughly with your legal adviser in advance.

While there is a variety of legal concerns and issues aging families need to consider, here is a separate, short list of some legal information that is valuable in relation to health care issues.

Legal Documents
- Powers of attorney[6]
- Advance directives and living wills[7]
- Health care surrogate designatee
- Long-term care and other insurance policies
- Social Security number
- Medicare number
- Medicare supplement policy
- Trust documents

Health Care Resources

Choosing a Primary Care Provider (PCP)

A common worry for many older adults as we deal with age-related health issues (and our sons and daughters often share this concern) is whether our primary care provider (PCP) is the best one for us at this point in our lives. Many of us have a PCP that we know and trust and who has known us for five, 10, sometimes 20 years, and we are reluctant to consider a change. This long-term relationship and the care provider's knowledge about our own unique medical history are very valuable.

On the other hand, many PCPs are not particularly knowledgeable about the unique medical needs of older people. It is especially problematic if the PCP is not up to date on the many medical advancements in the diagnosis and treatment of ailments common to older people. The field of geriatric medicine has benefited from enormous research

---

[6] See our handbook *Legal Issues of Aging Families* (forthcoming, Summer 2007) for an elaboration of these and other necessary legal documents, and legal issues commonly faced by aging families.
[7] Ibid.

in the past two decades and much is known now that was not a part of medical training a decade or two ago.

The following questions may help you assess whether to change PCPs, be pleased with the PCP you have, or keep your PCP but also get a consultation (or second opinion) from a specialist in geriatric medicine.

> **The field of geriatric medicine has benefited from enormous research in the past two decades and much is known now that was not a part of medical training a decade or two ago.**

- Is the PCP hurried, with no time for conversation?
- Does the PCP listen, and answer specific questions?
- Is there time available for follow-up questions?
- Does the PCP attribute your problems to "old age"?
- Does the PCP treat you with respect?
- Does the PCP take a detailed history and interview you thoroughly?
- Is the PCP knowledgeable about specific problems?
- Does the PCP answer all your questions and concerns?

Other Health Care Resources

In addition to having the right primary care provider, it is useful for you to become knowledgeable about some of the other health services frequently used by older adults. Many communities have at least one hospital that offers specialized services for older adults. These services may include classes and seminars on aging topics, support groups, as well as nurses, social workers, speech and physical therapists and other professionals who have special training and experience in the health care needs of older adults.

Often such hospitals have a monthly newsletter describing their classes, support groups and services for older adults. We recommend that you place yourself, your siblings, and your adult children on the mailing list. In this way all can learn about and become familiar with the health care-related topics and concerns that are discussed openly by others, which can help encourage open discussions in your family. Other organizations that commonly offer monthly educational mailings, classes and services include:

- Home health care providers
- Senior health programs within hospital centers
- Screening clinics for seniors
- Senior centers
- Adult day health programs
- Home chore and companion programs
- Accrediting agencies and associations, e.g., American Association of Homes and Services for the Aging

Become informed now. It is easier now than later, and your knowledge will benefit not only you but also your spouse and siblings, and your adult children, in the years ahead.

Seeking Advice from Experts

As we age we need to learn about the various types of professionals who are especially knowledgeable regarding legal, financial, insurance, health and social issues as they relate to older adults and aging families. Knowing the resources available to you and your adult children in your respective geographical areas is an important part of preparation. Most experts are open to a brief telephone or in-person interview and will provide references for you to contact. It is especially important to check on the reputation, integrity and experience of the professionals you engage.

Here is a brief list of the most common specialists who often serve as resources to aging families:

- A CPA or CFP who works with the elderly
- An attorney who specializes in eldercare and/or estate issues
- A long-term care insurance agent
- A physician who specializes in geriatrics
- A geriatric psychiatrist
- A geriatric care manager
- A geriatric family counselor

A geriatric care manager can help you take stock, develop a plan, identify resources needed, implement the plan, and monitor the progress of the plan, modifying it as needed. Geriatric care managers are usually nurses or social workers with years of experience in the home health care field. A geriatric family counselor is usually a social worker or psychologist trained and experienced in aging family dynamics, family communication and family conflict.

> **A geriatric care manager can help you take stock, develop a plan, identify resources needed, implement the plan, and monitor the progress of the plan, modifying it as needed.**

We invite you to become familiar with what each of these geriatric experts has to offer you and your intergenerational family. Our experience has been that even a single consultation with one or more of these experts can provide much-needed information and insights that will help you and your adult children continue to prepare for the changes and challenges ahead. Remember to take notes, and keep track of professionals' recommendations.

Knowing How You're Doing and Where You Need Assistance

Many older adults, in the privacy of our own minds, wonder how we are *really* doing. One inspiring example of dealing with this question proactively is a group of six older adults who, in addition to their ongoing relationships as one another's friends, schedule a meeting once a month just to discuss "how they're doing." They are totally honest. They share resources with each other, e.g., driving, shopping, tips on who is helpful for home repairs, etc. They hire a geriatric care manager to meet with them, together, every three months. They ask hard questions, welcome hard questions back, and support one another in putting into action any good suggestions they receive. They describe their commitment to the choice they have made to use honesty, friendship, staying informed, and finding good resources in order to remain as independent, safe and healthy as possible.

Part of a functional assessment includes reviewing a standardized list of what is called, in health care circles, Activities of Daily Living.

To ease your own mind there is no substitute for a good functional assessment, in addition to a good medical workup. Professional geriatric care managers perform these functional or "comprehensive" assessments. Part of a functional assessment includes reviewing a standardized list of what is called, in health care circles, "Activities of Daily Living." We list these below, as you may wish to begin to note and organize where you might need minor assistance in order to remain independent and also function satisfactorily in these essential daily activities.

List of Activities of Daily Living

- Cooking and food preparation: safety and hygiene; nutrition
- Eating: chewing and swallowing
- Bathing: safety and thoroughness
- Dressing: buttons, snaps, zippers, etc.
- Taking medications: remembering; taking too many or too few; refills
- Telephoning: your family, friends, 911
- Paying bills and managing money: making change, balancing books, safety and judgment
- Housekeeping: safety and cleanliness
- Shopping: driving, making change, food purchases, etc.

Keep a journal so you can note changes in your ability to perform these activities of daily living or note other important observations and changes. Furthermore, in relation to your spouse, it's important to observe rather than "do for," so you and he/she can get an accurate idea of the current level of functioning. When we're too quick to help or do something for a loved one, we lose the opportunity to make important observations. Spouses or siblings living together can be a team and help each other, but they also need to keep track honestly of what each person can and cannot do.

An ongoing journal of observations is one of the best ways to track how you are getting along. Be descriptive rather than evaluative in recording what you observe about yourself or your spouse or sibling. Making a judging statement such as "doing okay" or "getting by" is too imprecise to allow for a later comparison. Our memories are fallible and easily influenced by what we want to see or what we fear seeing. Also, unless you are very specific in describing what

Spouses or siblings living together can be a team and help each other, but they also need to keep track honestly of what each person can and cannot do.

you are able and not able to do, another person (e.g., sibling, adult child, or health care provider) who makes a later assessment cannot compare for improvement or worsening. Measurable comparisons are helpful to health care providers in accurately diagnosing issues.

Ideally, observations should be detailed and should include the date, time of day, and any notes on unusual circumstances. For example, if I have a bad cold my driving will probably be more erratic, perhaps my stops more abrupt, my attention to multiple sources of data at a busy intersection compromised, etc. If I see that's the case, I can then not drive until I feel competent and safe again. Observing yourself, or your spouse or sibling, following a recipe; wrapping Christmas gifts; writing a check; walking down the stairs into the basement; noting what food is placed in the refrigerator, what is left out and for how long are other sources of possible information. Safety in cooking and handling knives are other areas you might choose to check.

Involve others in helping you keep an eye on yourself. Neighbors, your old friends, and people who see you regularly welcome knowing that you care about yourself and that you want to know if they notice anything worrisome. The experience of one older woman, Louise, provides a good example of the value of recruiting others to help us.

In her 70s, and experiencing a lot of pain due to a hip that was in need of replacement, Louise became increasingly forgetful. Her friends worried and talked among themselves about it, but no one told her of their observations or concerns. Finally another friend of hers, someone whom she had not seen for several months, visited. He immediately knew something was wrong and said so; he insisted she see her doctor. In short, she was not developing Alzheimer's or dementia, but was losing her memory as a side effect of taking too much pain medicine. She cut back on the medicine, her memory came back, and she confronted her other friends: "Why didn't you tell me?" They all ended up promising one another to speak up about any changes they noted, and all were relieved.

As mentioned earlier in this handbook in the section on Behavioral and Cognitive Changes, some degree of forgetfulness and confusion is a natural part of aging, beginning in middle age. All too often this alarms us and we overreact by watching ourselves every moment and making a big deal out of normal forgetfulness. If you are concerned that either you or your spouse is experiencing problems with reasoning or memory, always assume first that the problem is caused by some other treatable condition and get an evaluation.

Our memories are fallible and easily influenced by what we want to see or what we fear seeing.

Remember to take your journal with you when you talk to your primary care provider or other health care providers, and keep notes of what they say.

Remember to take your journal with you when you talk to your primary care provider or other health care providers, and keep notes of what they say. Learn from relatives and friends who are also part of aging families. Continually learn about aging. Become an expert. Become a role model. Finally, talk with professionals and/or geriatric healthcare experts if you feel concern. They discuss these issues every day and have a wealth of experience and expertise.

Tips for Tough Conversations About Health Care Issues

First, you can expect that your children's pace will be faster than yours. Many of the decisions you face will change your life, so it's no surprise that you might want to take your time making them. You may experience some anxiety, and need to manage your feelings and the pace of any decisions. Many older adults report that first thinking and talking things through with an eldercare consultant helps a great deal. Most importantly, keep in mind the big picture of your relationship with your family members.

While by no means a "cure all," we have found that the following tips from our handbook *The Dynamics of Aging Families* will help difficult family conversations start out and stay on the right track.

- Arrange the best time and place for everyone involved in the discussion.
- Think through and, ideally, discuss with someone else (spouse, friend, adviser) what you plan to say.

- Share observations, information, concerns and resources.

- Be prepared to plant seeds for consideration regarding decisions or actions to be taken at a later date.

- First and foremost, be a good listener. Try to understand the other person's position from his or her point of view before presenting your own.

- Assure that everyone is heard.

- Involve the family in decisions.

- Keep your shared values in mind. We often focus on our differing solutions to a problem when in fact we share similar values about the issue.

- Communicate your respect and caring. Express affection and appreciation. Protect the larger and ongoing relationship.

When Your Adult Children Live Far Away

When your adult children live far away, you face special challenges. Remember the issues Mary and Joe and their family faced in the scenario we looked at earlier, where the parents lived at a distance from their children? Often you worry about your adult sons, daughters, and your grandkids, and they worry about you. All too often they withhold their concerns, problems and life challenges "so as not to worry you," just as you don't mention your concerns, problems and life challenges "so as not to worry them." This form of love, or protective caring, unfortunately often has some very negative consequences. You don't truly know how they're doing or if you can help in any way. They don't truly know how you're doing, either. Often when we need each other most, no one knows.

We believe there is great value in both generations being open and honest with each other. Each may or may not be able to provide concrete, tangible assistance to the other. But both sides will have the opportunity to care, to love, to support, encourage and "believe in" their other family members.

Usually your children want to help, to give back, and want to feel confident that you have access to the care and help you need. If you've always taken pride in your independence and self-sufficiency, you may find it takes a lot of courage to swallow your pride and accept some help. Do it. You will discover that you can actually do even better with a little help. Further, think of it as a gift to your children. They can worry less,

> **If you've always taken pride in your independence and self-sufficiency, you may find it takes a lot of courage to swallow your pride and accept some help.**

relax more, and their interactions with you will be less filled with their concerns, worries, and efforts to find out how you're doing.

Finally, develop good friendships. Learn about social, health care, financial and legal resources for older adults. The more you develop a good "team" to support you as you age, the more your adult children can continue to relate to you as they always have.

Should A Crisis Occur…

The best possible outcome of working through the questions in this handbook and its three companion handbooks is that, should a health crisis occur, you and your family will have a strong support system in place to manage it. That support system will include pertinent, updated personal, financial, legal and health care-related information, in addition to helpful people. While we hope a crisis will never happen, here are a few additional tips and questions, based on the experiences of other older adults, to help guide you if it does.

- Expect sudden and severe stress. Learn stress-relieving techniques that work for you.
- Remember that talking helps. And that the collective IQ is usually higher than yours alone.
- Remember to watch your diet, exercise and rest during times of stress.
- Pace yourself. This may last longer than you think.

Guiding Questions:
- How might your life change? In the short run? In the long run?

- Will the situation improve or get worse? Consult experts if needed.

- Will care in your own home be financially and logistically feasible?

- Might the necessary care require relocation? Temporary? Permanent?

- Do you need an eldercare consultation? They may help you ask "what if" questions and prepare for several possible or likely scenarios.

- How can you best use the information you have collected thus far?

Practical Needs in Case of a Health Crisis

After a health crisis involving their parents, many adult children have suggested to us that it would have been helpful to have had, or had access to, the following things.

- Your house key and code for alarm system, if applicable
- Keys to your car if needed
- Name and phone number of your next-door neighbors, or people they might need to contact immediately in the event of an emergency
- List of people to notify, with phone numbers

There are many more possible items to add to this list; you can use it as a point of departure to prepare something suitable for your own particular needs.

Again, we hope you will never need these. But from our own trips to emergency rooms with aging parents and stories from our clients who are sons and daughters, we've learned that all too often you will need to be prepared for the possibility of a six- to 12-hour ordeal. If you are the spouse or sibling going along, take your cell phone, address book, a sweater, food bars, something to drink, funds for snack bars and vending machines, information about their prescription and non-prescription medicines, and your own prescription medicines: these are a few of the basics. Set aside some time now to take note of your own needs, so you can be prepared. Have a small suitcase or large handbag ready. You will want to be able to grab your bag and go.

> **Set aside some time now to take note of your own needs, so you can be prepared. Have a small suitcase or large handbag ready.**

Care Receiving and Caregiving

Our society has given care receiving—being the person who is in need of care—a bad reputation. The extreme value we place on independence and self-reliance is partially to blame. The truth is that throughout our lives from birth to death there is ebb and flow, give and take, to when we give care and when we receive care. We have observed, through our clients' and friends' experience and from our own personal experience, both the joys and hardships of caregiving and the joys and hardships of care receiving.

Just as in other areas of life, if you are open to learning and willing to risk honest communication regarding caregiving and care receiving, you can get better at both. You can learn from the experience of others. Be curious when a friend, family member or neighbor is giving or receiving care. Put yourself in the other's place. Imagine how you might bring your own unique personality and experience to bear. Set aside the stories you tell yourself about yourself, and explore what is really true for you right now.

Below we offer some tips on caregiving and care receiving. However, we urge you to go further: read books, practice in small ways, take seminars, talk with others and truly learn and prepare for the care receiving and the caregiving that's ahead. There are many excellent books about each side of caring, and some are listed in our bibliography.[8]

Tips for Care Receiving

- Ask directly for what you need. Few of us can read minds.

- Learn to openly discuss what you may need. Thinking it through with someone else often results in better decisions.

- If you try to be more independent and self-reliant than is possible you'll make things worse.

- Relax. Enjoy the parts you can. If you've got to receive help, your relaxation, enjoyment and appreciation is a gift both to yourself and to the caregiver.

- Learn as much as you can about your illness or condition.

- Whenever possible, emotionally hard as it maybe, add new helpers to your care team.[9] You'll benefit and you'll help take good care of your current care team members.

- Talk with others, join a support group and learn as much as you can from other care receivers. We don't have to learn everything ourselves the hard way, through trial and error!

---

[8] See especially *Counting on Kindness: The Dilemmas of Dependency* by Wendy Lustbader and *Tuesdays with Morrie* by Mitch Albom.

[9] See *Personal Safety Nets: Getting Ready for Life's Inevitable Changes and Challenges* by John W. Gibson and Judy Pigott, for a "how to" on recruiting and managing a care sharing team for the caregiving journey.

- Retain, discover, and add to areas of your life in which you can still engage. These nourish you, give you things to talk about, and take you away from your troubles.

Tips for Caregiving

- Be honest with yourself about your capabilities.

- Regularly take stock of the care receiver's needs and of your needs.

- Talk with others.

- Know your limits and keep them.

- Get help early in the process.

- It takes a whole community to support a caregiver and their care receiver. Start forming a team now!

- Learn about the care receiver's illness or condition.

- Take breaks from the very start. Most caregiving goes on for much longer than you expected.

When you are providing health care support for a loved one, it is important to recognize and manage the additional stress this adds to your life. We can't emphasize enough that it is crucial to balance your needs with the care receiver's needs from the very start, and to retain your own life-enriching activities.

On average, most of us will spend between 10 and 20 years of our adult lives giving care to other adults, usually relatives. Most of us will also be receiving some care for an extended period.

On average most of us will spend between 10 and 20 years of our adult lives giving care to other adults, usually relatives. Most of us will also be receiving some care for an extended period. So learn, practice, become an expert; you and your loved ones will be glad you did.

Common Senior Housing Options

Most of us prefer to live at home as we age. However, the day may come when your circumstances change and your living situation doesn't seem to work any more. This could be due to the death of a spouse or to a debilitating illness that limits your mobility and your ability to care for yourself. Or you may simply want to give up some of the responsibilities involved in maintaining a home so you can focus your time and energy on other activities.

You can begin now to plan ahead and sort through various options. Gather information early, while you are healthy and not under undo pressure, and decisions can be made at a comfortable pace. Visiting many places, and taking a friend or adult child along, can be helpful.

The following list of questions will help you determine what is important to you, and will help you (and, if you wish, your adult children) identify and evaluate potential new living situations.

- Will you be accessible to your friends or to people with whom you could make new friendships?

- Will you be close to family?

- Will you have access to favorite stores, public transportation, and other services you are accustomed to using?

- How much living space do you need?

- How much privacy do you need?

- Will you be able to have pets, personal furnishings, and other desired items with you?

- Are the bedroom and bathroom easily accessible now, and would they continue to be in case of increased limitation in mobility?

- Will doctors, pharmacists and health care services be available?

- Will you have adequate opportunity to form new relationships?

- What are the costs associated with the proposed housing?

- Talking with several other people who have made such a move can be informative and will help you consider various perspectives.

Should You Move In With Your Adult Children?

For some older people, moving in with their adult children is their first choice when living alone is no longer possible. For others, it may be a difficult choice or their last choice. If you are considering moving in with your adult child, you need to talk seriously

> **Each of you needs to be sure to express all your feelings about the situation before making any decisions.**

with that child and their family members to understand how each one of them feels. Each of you needs to be sure to express all your feelings about the situation before making any decisions. Talk with friends who live with an adult child and try to understand what it is like for them. Have your children do the same with any peers of theirs who live with their older parent(s). Think through these questions and discuss the issues together before agreeing to the move.

- Do you really want to live with your adult child? Have you been honest with yourself and them about your feelings about it?

- Have you talked with them about what to expect and why? If yes, are you satisfied with the dialogue? If no, when and how will you do that?

- How much time can you comfortably spend with your child and the family? Have you explained what your weeks and weekends are like in detail? Do you know about theirs?

- Can you afford it? What financial arrangements would be made with them?

- Are you aware of local services that could help you through difficult situations?

Sharing a Home

You may choose to consider sharing your home with others, moving into someone else's home, or finding a new house that can accommodate you and others of your choice.

Shared households can be arranged in any number of ways: for example, by sharing expenses or by exchanging services, or by renting. Any arrangements should be put in writing so there will be no misunderstandings later.

Questions to Consider:

• Would you want to share your home or move to share another's home? If so, how would daily life change?

• How might sharing a home affect your finances?

• How might you divide household duties and finances?

• How might you resolve differences that arise?

• What might your responsibility be if your housemate becomes ill?

Adult Family Homes

Adult family homes generally provide a room, meals, utilities, housekeeping and laundry, and staff to give whatever assistance is needed. State laws usually specify how many adults can live in each home.

Visit several homes, with a friend or your adult children, before deciding. Look at the room you may occupy, meet the other residents, and have a meal there. Ask lots of questions about the services and evaluate the staff. Ask for references and check the home's record with the local or state licensing agency and the Long-Term Care Ombudsman Office. Adult family homes are the least regulated type of senior housing.

Questions to Consider:

• Will you have privacy and independence?

• How much will it cost, including add-ons to the rent?

• Is it near public transportation, places of worship, and shopping?

• Can the home meet your special dietary needs?

• Does the home comply with local licensing, fire and zoning laws? Is it licensed by the state?

• What are the arrangements for sharing bathrooms?

• Will you have to climb stairs?

• Are there security locks on each room?

• Will you have access to a telephone?

• Are pets allowed? If so, who will care for them?

Retirement Communities/Congregate Housing

Retirement communities usually include an apartment, condominium or townhouse complex. Most serve meals in a central dining room, and provide housekeeping services. Each unit includes a kitchen. Many retirement communities provide a professional staff, such as social workers, counselors, or nutritionists. Congregate housing facilities (another term that is sometimes used to describe group housing) are sponsored by non-profit and for-profit agencies.

Questions to Consider:

- What are the other residents like?

- Is transportation to stores, places of worship, and other services available?

- Can the facility accommodate your special dietary needs?

- What in-house services are available? Look for services such as occupational and physical therapy, counseling, recreational and social activities, and a library.

- What is the cost of additional health care services? Be sure to check for all costs in advance.

- What are the policies on bringing one's own furniture?

- Are pets allowed?

- How do you, your friends, and your adult children feel about the overall atmosphere of the facility?

Continuing Care Retirement and Assisted Living Communities

Most continuing care retirement communities offer the benefits of independent living in apartments and houses. However, they also include health care services, assisted living, and a skilled nursing facility on the premises. The cost of continuing care retirement communities varies widely. In some communities you "buy in" with an entrance fee (which may or may not be refundable) and you also pay monthly fees. With others there is simply a rental fee.

Questions to Consider:
- What medical costs and services are covered?

- What is the policy for moving between different levels of care?

- How does management respond to resident concerns?

- What costs do the fees cover?

- What transportation to needed services is available? How frequently? At what cost?

• What is the refund policy for deposits and entrance fees?

• What is the history of increases in monthly fees?

• Is the facility financially stable enough to outlive you?[10]

Nursing Homes

Nursing homes are only for those who have seriously illness and/or require skilled nursing services.

There are many choices to make regarding where and how to live as you age. In your mind's eye, put yourself in each of the living environments described and try to imagine how you might feel living there. Focus on your quality of life, your sense of security and well-being, and the place's capacity to help you respond to the changes in your life as you age. Be proactive about the choices you make about where to live. Your choice will affect every other part of your life.

---

[10] For more detail on this topic, see our companion handbook *Financial Issues of Aging Families.*

III: The Health Care Issues Brainstorming Journal

Hopefully you have been answering the questions posed in this handbook as you have gone along. The following questions are intended to help deepen your understanding, and build on the information you have gathered so far. We hope they will stimulate additional questions for you to ask and answer.

- What are the optimal ways you can help manage your changing health care needs?

- What are your greatest concerns about your health care needs?

- How can you, your adult children, and your health care provider function as a care sharing team?

- What additional questions might you ask to gather more information for yourself about your changing health care needs?

- Do you want to give your health care providers permission so they can communicate directly with your adult children if necessary? Your permission will need to be in writing.

- Do you understand your health insurance, Medicare and Medicaid benefits and how to process your paperwork to get coverage? If not, do you have resources to help you manage that?

- If you were no longer able to communicate verbally or in writing, do you feel comfortable that someone you trust understands your short and long-term health care needs? If not, how might you bring about this understanding?

- If you were no longer able to see well enough to read or watch TV, how would you stay mentally engaged in your daily life? Would you enjoy listening to books or music on tape or CDs? Would you enjoy having someone read to you?

IV: Action Plan for Getting Started

The focus of this handbook has been on helping you prepare to meet the changes and challenges you may face in dealing with health care issues. Because you are much more likely to make the best of these changes and challenges when you have anticipated, planned, and prepared for them ahead of time, this action plan provides you with a framework to get your planning started.

Action Planning Steps: Overview

We have found these six steps to be a valuable tool for focusing and organizing your planning. We invite you to use them as they are or to modify them to suit your unique needs.

1. Create a contingency plan for managing short- and long-term changes in your health.

2. Identify and answer questions related to your contingency plan, including:

   a. Questions you can't answer because you don't have enough information.

   b. Questions you can answer that highlight your need to take corrective action.

   c. Questions whose answers you know but haven't shared with loved ones.

3. Identify specific, timely, realistic goals whose outcomes you can measure using three-month, six-month and one-year timelines.

4. Track your progress in writing.

5. Take one step at a time to work on this action plan incrementally.

6. Allow yourself to ask for and receive help from others as you age, so that you are also caring for yourself.

Developing a Plan to Meet Your Current and Near-Future Health Care Needs

- What's most important?

- Be honest with yourself and your family about your health care needs.

- Adopt an experimental attitude about ways in which your health care needs can be met, perhaps with help from your adult children and your health care professionals. Think in terms of your health care team.

- List what you need for optimal health care even if you don't know how you can meet this need.

- Consider professional consultation for the entire family. A large family meeting with a good eldercare consultant often results in open, respectful discussion on difficult issues, and helps you work together as a team.

Identifying Key Questions to Address

- Medical, legal, and financial needs

- Activities of daily living

- Social needs

- Housing modifications

- Other needs

- Others' involvement in planning

Putting the Plan into Action

- Who, what, when, where?

- For how long?

- How to recognize if it's not working.

- What needs changing?

- Keep logs.

- Put things in writing.

- Be specific.

- Be honest.

Within Three Months

If this book is truly to guide you through making the best decisions regarding your health care, then you have to begin the work now. The following topics and questions are intended to get you started. Write out answers to the questions, create the lists, identify and secure the resources, consult with trusted advisers, and above all, take responsibility and control of planning and preparing for your health care needs.

- Create lists. Begin collecting information for your Personal Documents List and Personal Support System List.

- Collect data.

- Begin conversations.

- Address related legal concerns and issues.[11]

- Address related financial concerns and issues.[12]

- Address concerns and issues relating to family dynamics.[13]

Take Stock of Your Current Health Situation

- How would you evaluate your own health/illness status? In regard to "Activities of Daily Living," what is your level of ability on each activity?

- Can your functioning and strengths be increased? How?

- Scrutinize your attitudes, beliefs, expectations and paradigms as they relate to aging, abilities and disabilities. Do you have any self-defeating attitudes or beliefs? How can you change them? What new attitudes do you want to establish?

- Talk with friends and family about helping you monitor your health and other needs. Create your own "team" and "buddies."

---

[11] See *Legal Issues of Aging Families.*
[12] See *Financial Issues of Aging Families.*
[13] See *The Dynamics of Aging Families.*

Educate Yourself About Aging and Related Resources

- Research to see if there are social networks you might enjoy that combine physical and mental fitness activities with opportunities to become more involved in your community.

- Subscribe yourself, your friends, and your adult children to mailing lists that educate and offer services and classes related to older adults and their adult children.

- Do the same with newsletters related to aging well and to reducing your risk factors. It's never too late to become as healthy as you can.

- Learn ways to grow stronger and/or preserve your areas of high function. Use it, so you don't lose it.

- Identify environmental modifications to make your living and working environments more "elder-friendly."

Within Six Months

Remember, some of the actions you took in the first three months are either ongoing or may require further attention or need to be revised.

Re-Think Your Health Care Values, Beliefs and Preferences

- Receiving care: how easy is it now for you to allow others to care for you?

- How can you learn to be better at asking for and receiving help? Not a bit more than you need, nor any less than you need.

- How can you begin to look for ways to maintain an acceptable quality of life if your physical and/or mental capacities diminish? Keep discovering the things that really matter to you!

- How can you learn to manage reduced energy reserves?

- What is your wish list of special activities that will bring joy and meaning to your life?

- What are your top priorities for the years you may have left? How can you assure you have the time and energy you need to give to these priorities?

- How can you be smart about aging, and strategically compensate for age-related changes?

- What do you need to learn and plan for in regard to your illness(es)— options, probable course, best and worst case scenarios?

- How have you communicated with key people in your life about your situation in a realistic and mature way?

- Create a file of model "Help Appeal" letters, phone tree names and numbers, and scripts for conversations about tough topics, so that you are ready (while at the same time you're hoping you will never need them).[14] Think of this as your non-financial life insurance policy. Keep all of this information in a file that is easy to access and update.

- Acknowledge the areas in which you are dependent upon your spouse and/or adult children. Recognize that doing this takes guts and courage. Find ways to express your gratitude.

Within One Year

- Have a care sharing team or supporting resource people in place (while hoping you never need them).

- Implement mature interdependence and mature dependence in your life style, health care activities, and with friends and family.

---

[14] For examples of "Help Appeal" letters and phone call scripts, see *Personal Safety Nets: Getting Ready for Life's Inevitable Changes and Challenges.*

- Have legal affairs that impact health care in order with advisers and family.

- Have financial affairs that impact health care in order with advisers and family.

- Continue to implement the attitudes, beliefs and paradigms that suggest possibilities, promise and opportunities to make the years ahead the best possible. Be honest about aging, but also enjoy today and make plans to enjoy tomorrow.

- You should be seeing some of the positive results of your planning process!

- Continue to gather information and make plans.

V: Questions for Your Health Care Provider(s) and Advisers

- Do you know of other health care providers/advisers who have expertise with age-related health care issues whom you would recommend?

- What training have you received in health care issues of older adults?

- What percentage of your patient base is facing the health care issues that I face?

- How have other patients like me dealt with similar health care issues? What were the outcomes?

- Do you know of things I can do to retain my health as long as possible? If so, what do you suggest?

- Do you use a team approach to address health care issues for older adults and their families?

- What professional limits or confidentiality constraints do you have regarding working with my family and me? How can we address these if we wish to take a family approach?

Authors' Biographies

John W. Gibson, DSW, has more than 25 years experience as a consultant, therapist, coach and mediator focusing on family issues of health, aging and inter-generational communication. John is a former faculty member of Columbia University and University of Washington, is a specialist in aging, and is in private practice in Seattle, Washington.

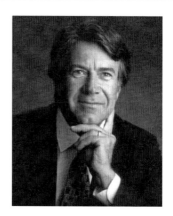

Bonnie Brown Hartley, Ph.D., is President of Transition Dynamics Inc., a consulting firm specializing in business family and organizational transitions. Bonnie works primarily on planning, communication and relationship management in two areas: business family governance systems and life-long learning maps for developing interests and competencies in multigenerational business family teams.

Photo by Andrew Kent